SYMPHONY
IN F MINOR

❀

By R. VAUGHAN WILLIAMS

Full Score
Price 12s. 6d.

OXFORD UNIVERSITY PRESS
36 Soho Square London W.1

INSTRUMENTATION

Flute I
Flute II and Piccolo
Flute III (*ad lib.*)
Oboe I
Oboe II (*ad lib.*—except in Scherzo)
Cor Anglais and Oboe III (Oboe III *ad lib.* in Scherzo)
Clarinets I and II
Bass Clarinet (*ad lib.*)
Fagotti I and II
Contra fagotto (*ad lib.*)
Horns I, II, III, IV
Trumpets I and II
Trombones I, II, III
Tuba
Timpani (chromatic *ad lib.*)
Percussion : Side Drum, Triangle, Cymbals, Bass Drum
(Two players required)
Violins I and II
Viole
Violoncelli
Contra Bassi

Time of performance : approximately 32 minutes.
Orchestral material can be hired from the Publishers,
including large-size Full Scores if preferred.

———————

———————

This Symphony was first given at a B.B.C. Symphony
Concert, April 10, 1935, conducted by Sir Adrian Boult.
It is recorded by H.M.V. with the B.B.C. Symphony
Orchestra conducted by the Composer.

To Arnold Bax

SYMPHONY IN F MINOR
IN FOUR MOVEMENTS

I

R. VAUGHAN WILLIAMS

OXFORD UNIVERSITY PRESS, AMEN HOUSE, WARWICK SQUARE, E.C.4.

4

8

13

14

24

25

27

II

31

33

34

36

39

III
SCHERZO

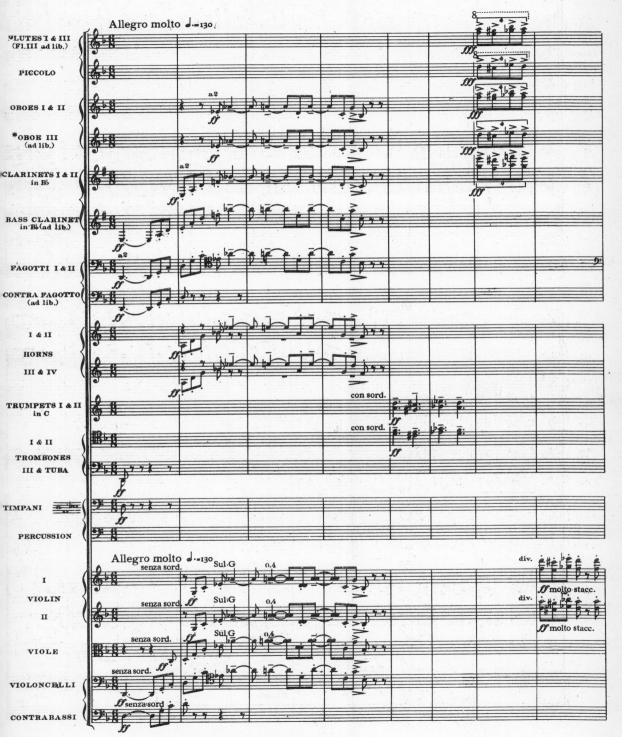

*NOTE. In this movement Oboe II is obbligato and Oboe III ad lib.

43

45

48

52

55

56

57

61

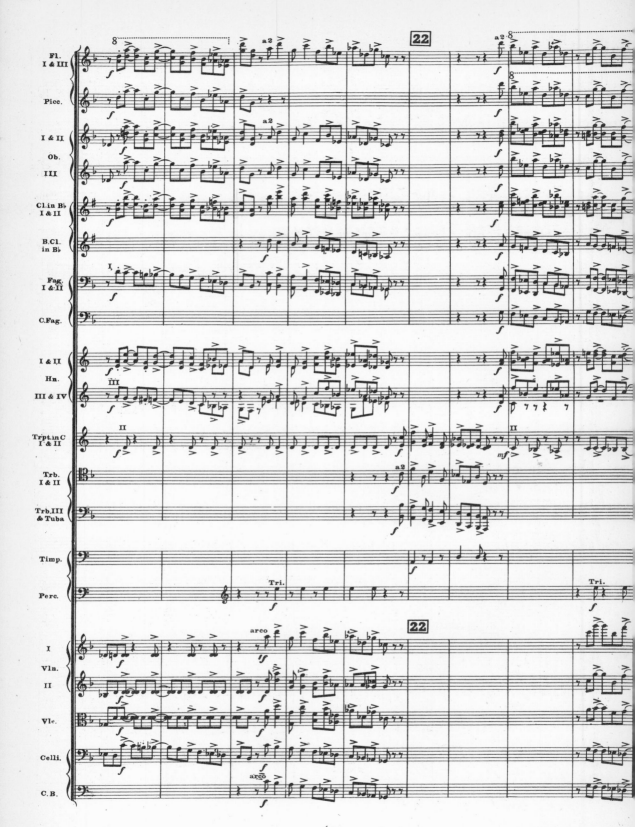

66

67

71

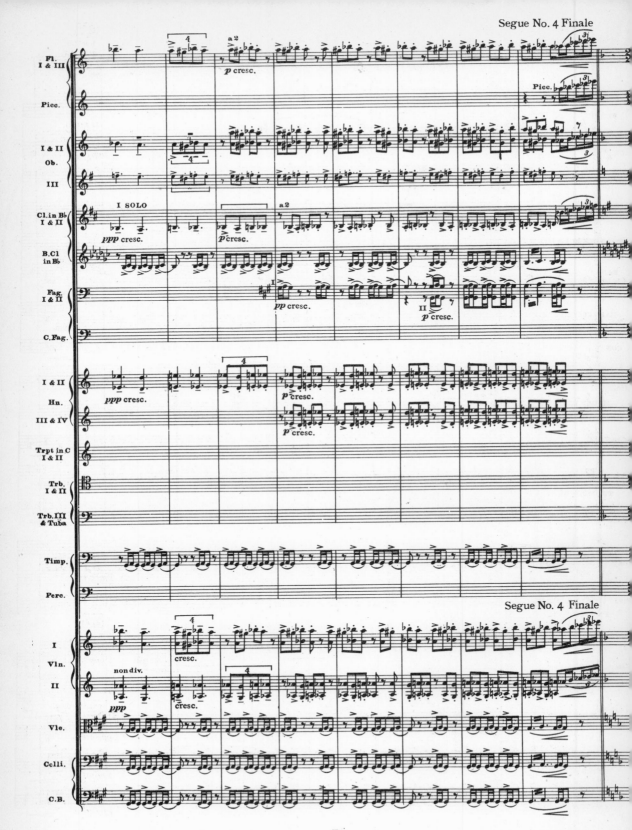

Segue No. 4 Finale

IV
FINALE CON EPILOGO FUGATO

79

84

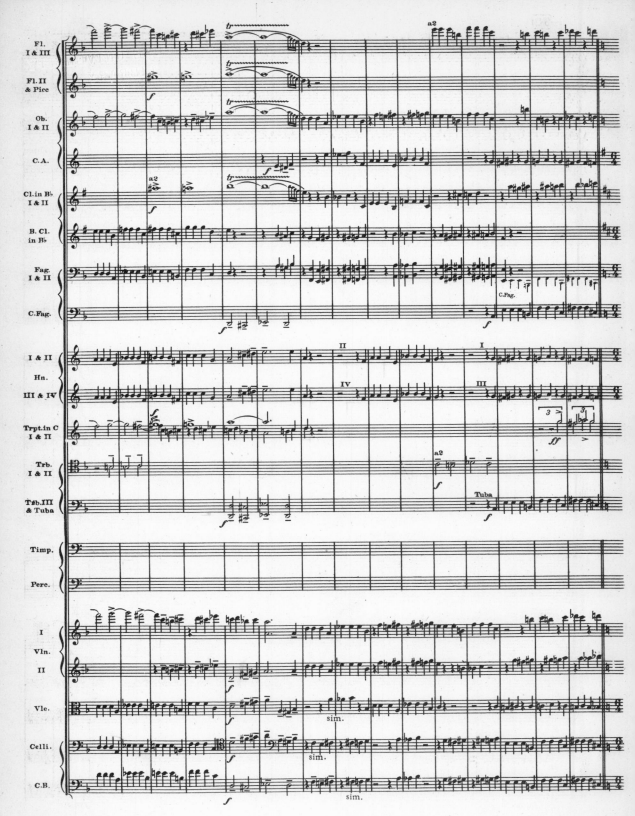

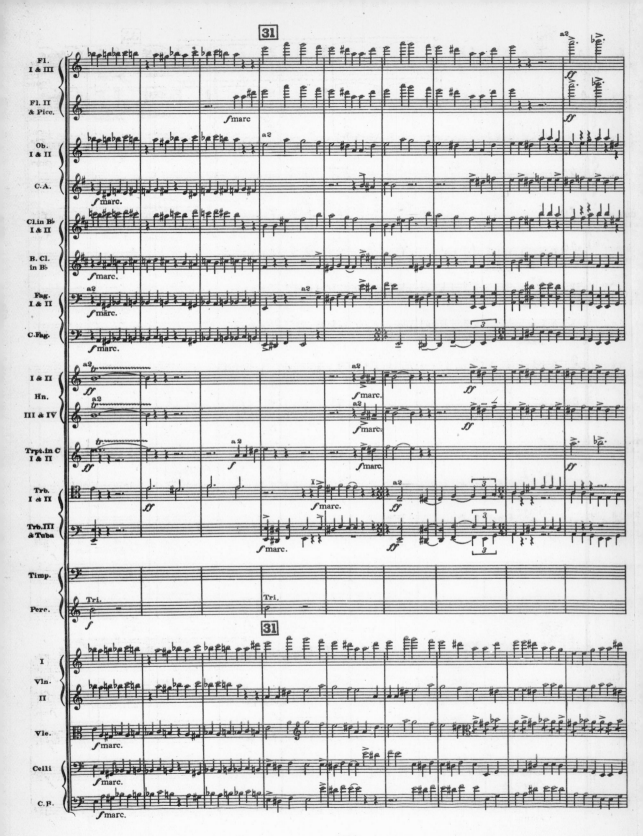